A MAN NAMED NOAH

The Story of the Great Flood and God's Promise

Genesis 6:9–9:17 for children

Written by Karen N. Sanders
Illustrated by Marcy Ramsey

CONCORDIA PUBLISHING HOUSE · SAINT LOUIS

A long time ago, was a man named Noah
Who loved and worshiped God.
This faithful man followed God's commands
Even when they seemed quite odd!

Most people had become very bad.
They ignored their Creator Lord.
They were full of vice, laughed at God's advice,
Spreading hate, which God deplored.

"Noah," with dread, God sadly said,
"I've decided to make it rain.
A flood will swirl over the entire world
And get rid of sin and pain.

"I'll wash the world clean, no one will be seen—
Just you and your family of eight.
But you'll need to embark, build an awesome ark
Immediately! Don't wait!"

"I will not ask why," was Noah's reply.
"I'll do as You instruct,
With the helping hands of my family band
An ark we shall construct."

With pegs and boards, Noah learned from the Lord
Exactly what to do—
What wood to prize, what shape and size;
God's ship just grew and grew!

"You're sick in the head!" the neighbors said,
"To build that big ship here!
Where will it float, that gigantic boat,
That you've worked on year by year?"

Then God said, "My son, your work's nearly done.
Your humongous ark is strong.
Now search trees and lairs for thousands of pairs
Of creatures to bring along."

Arriving by twos, they walked, crawled, and flew,
The animals, from lions to mice.
When God shut the door at the thunder's roar,
Noah was glad for His advice.

Rain caused great fright forty days and nights,
Flooding low and high.
The waters came down over forest and town,
But the ark stayed snug and dry.

Imagine the hoots and snorts and toots
Of those animals large and small:
The lions that roared, birds and bees that soared,
Our Lord God loved them all.

God stopped the rain, but the ark remained
Afloat for months after that.
Then it hit—ker-plop! upon the top
Of the mount called Ararat.

Next God's wind blew and the sea withdrew.
Noah sent out a dove,
That returned with a leaf, to the crew's relief,
A sign of the Lord's great love.

Noah's family at last was free,
And stepped out on the land quite dry.
They worshiped God with praises loud,
As a rainbow filled the sky.

God promised then that never again
Would He flood the entire earth.
Now our faith we base on baptismal grace,
And the gift of Jesus' birth.

Our water comes down from a Christ-based crown.
God's love makes us remark,
"Since You say so, Lord, we'll trust You, Lord,
Like Noah, who built the ark."

Dear Parents,

Children and all animal lovers enjoy the story of Noah's ark. Thousands of animals peacefully enter a boat bigger than a football stadium and float to safety. But this story has a dark side: God was so disappointed by the people He had created that He decided to destroy most life on earth! But because God promised, your child does not need to worry about another worldwide flood.

When you talk about the story of Noah with your child, emphasize that God loved the world and its creations so much that He chose to give us a fresh start with faithful, obedient Noah and a sampling of every animal that inhabited earth. Also, God promised never to destroy the world by flood again. Talk about this promise the next time you and your child see a rainbow.

If your child wonders, a "cubit" is 18 inches. Noah's ark was six times as long as it was wide (450 feet x 75 feet), the same proportions used by modern shipbuilders. Scholars have estimated that about 45,000 animals could have fit in the ark!

Matthew 24:37–44 relates our preparedness for Christ's second coming to Noah's readiness for the flood. Emphasize with your child how we can communicate with God through prayer. However, we should not only pray to God; we also need to listen. Like Noah, we need to listen for God's instructions in the Bible and be ready to follow. We, too, need to reply, "If You say so, Lord!"

God washed the earth clean with a big flood of water. Even if we sometimes misbehave, because of Jesus' sacrifice for us, God forgives us and keeps us in His family. How reassuring is this promise!

The Author